This edition published 1995 by Geddes & Grosset Ltd, David Dale House, New Lanark, Scotland

Illustrated by Lyndsay Duff in the style of Charles Robinson

ISBN 1 85534 556 0

Printed in Slovenia

Mother Goose Rhymes

Old
Mother
Hubbard
Mother Hubbard's old dog Tray.
If this account be true,
Had not an equal, I dare say,
Come tell me, what think you?

Old Mother Hubbard

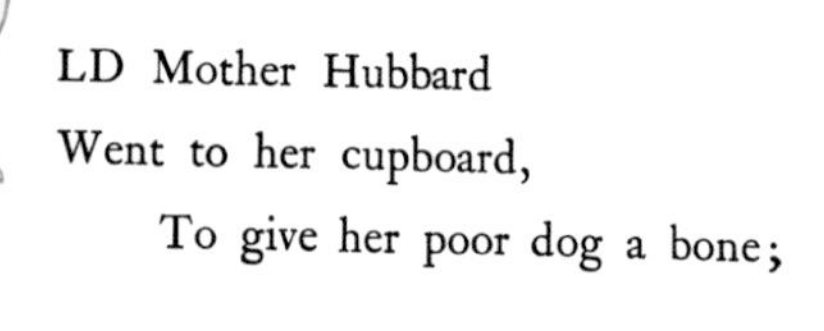

OLD Mother Hubbard
Went to her cupboard,
To give her poor dog a bone;

When she came there
The cupboard was bare,
And so the poor dog had none.

She went to the baker's
To buy him some bread,
When she came back
The dog was dead!

She went to the undertaker's
To buy him a coffin;
When she came back
The dog was laughing.

She took a clean dish
To get him some tripe;
When she came back
He was smoking his pipe.

She went to the ale-house
To get him some beer;
When she came back
The dog sat in a chair.

She went to the tavern
For white wine and red;
When she came back
The dog stood on his head.

She went to the hatter's
To buy him a hat;
When she came back
He was feeding the cat.

She went to the barber's
To buy him a wig;
When she came back
He was dancing a jig.

She went to the fruiterer's
To buy him some fruit;
When she came back
He was playing the flute.

She went to the tailor's
To buy him a coat;
When she came back
He was riding a goat.

Old Mother Hubbard

She went to the cobbler's
To buy him some shoes;
When she came back
He was reading the news.

She went to the sempster's
To buy him some linen;
When she came back
The dog was spinning.

She went to the hosier's
To buy him some hose;
When she came back
He was dressed in his clothes.

The dame made a curtsy,
The dog made a bow;
The dame said, "Your servant,"
The dog said, "Bow-wow!"

TO BABYLON

HOW many miles is it to Babylon?
  Threescore miles and ten.
Can I get there by candle-light?
  Yes, and back again!
If your heels are nimble and light,
You may get there by candle-light.

MY BLACK HEN

Hickety, pickety, my black
  hen,
She lays eggs for gentlemen;
Gentlemen come every day
To see what my black hen
  doth lay.

I'LL TELL YOU A STORY

I 'll tell you a story
About Jack a Nory—
And now my story 's begun:

I 'll tell you another,
About Jack his brother—
And now my story 's done.

THREE SHIPS

I SAW three ships come sailing by,
Sailing by, sailing by,
I saw three ships come sailing by,
On New-Year's day in the morning?

And what do you think was in them then,
In them then, in them then?
And what do you think was in them then,
On New-Year's day in the morning?

Three pretty girls were in them then,
In them then, in them then,
Three pretty girls were in them then,
On New-Year's day in the morning.

And one could whistle, and one could sing,
And one could play on the violin,
Such joy there was at my wedding,
On New-Year's day in the morning.

DING, DONG, BELL.

Ding, dong, bell, the cat is in the well!
Who put her in? Little Johnny Green.

Who pulled her out?
Little Tommy Stout.
What a naughty boy was that,
To try to drown poor pussy cat,
Who never did him any harm,
But killed the mice in his father's barn!

BOBBY SNOOKS

LITTLE BOBBY SNOOKS was fond of his books,
And loved by his usher and master;

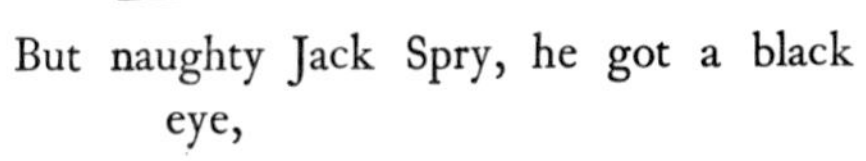

But naughty Jack Spry, he got a black eye,
And carries his nose in a plaster.

SIX LITTLE MICE

Six little mice sat down to spin,
Pussy passed by, and she peeped in.
"What are you at, my little men?"
"Making coats for gentlemen."
"Shall I come in and bite off your threads?"
"No, no, Miss Pussy, you 'll bite off our heads."
"Oh, no, I 'll not, I 'll help you spin."
"That may be so, but you don't come in."

WING, WANG, WADDLE, OH

MY father he died, but I can't tell you how,
He left me six horses to drive in my plough;
With my wing, wang, waddle, oh,
Jack sing saddle, oh,
Blowsey boys buble, oh,
Under the broom.

I sold my six horses and I bought me a cow,
I'd fain have made a fortune but did not know how:
With my wing, wang, waddle, oh,
Jack sing saddle, oh,
Blowsey boys buble, oh,
Under the broom.

I sold my cow, and I bought me a calf;
I'd fain have made a fortune but lost the best half;

With my wing, wang, waddle, oh,
Jack sing saddle, oh,
Blowsey boys buble, oh,
Under the broom.

I sold my calf, and I bought me a cat;
A pretty thing she was, in my chimney corner sat;
With my wing, wang, waddle, oh,
Jack sing saddle oh,
Blowsey boys buble, oh,
Under the broom.

I sold my cat and bought me a mouse;
He carried fire in his tail, and burnt down my house;
With my wing, wang, waddle, oh,
Jack sing saddle, oh,
Blowsey boys buble, oh,
Under the broom.

THE HART

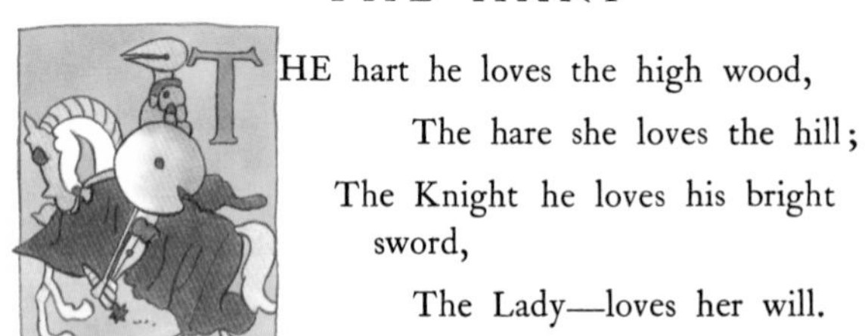

THE hart he loves the high wood,
The hare she loves the hill;
The Knight he loves his bright sword,
The Lady—loves her will.

OLD CHAIRS TO MEND

IF I'd as much money as I could spend,
I never would cry old chairs to mend;
Old chairs to mend, old chairs to mend;
I never would cry old chairs to mend.

If I'd as much money as I could tell,
I never would cry old clothes to sell;
Old clothes to sell, old clothes to sell;
I never would cry old clothes to sell.

SEE, SEE!

See, see! what shall I see?
A horse's head where his tail should be!

DICKERY, DICKERY, DARE

Dickery,
dickery,
dare,

The
pig
flew
up
in
the
air;

The
man
in
brown
soon
brought
him
down,

Dickery,
dickery,
dare.

COCK-CROW.

COCKS crow in the morn
To tell us to rise,
And he who lies late
Will never be wise;

For early to bed
And early to rise,
Is the way to be healthy
And wealthy and wise.

COCK ROBIN'S COURTING

Cock Robin got up early,
At the break of day,
And went to Jenny's window
To sing a roundelay.

He sang Cock Robin's love
To the little Jenny Wren,
And when he got unto the end,
Then he began again.

PUNCH AND JUDY

Punch and Judy
  Fought for a pie,
Punch gave Judy
  A knock in the eye.

Says Punch to Judy,
  "Will you have any more?"
Says Judy to Punch,
  "My eye is too sore."

LADY-BIRD, LADY-BIRD

Lady-Bird, Lady-Bird, fly away
home,
Your house is on fire, your children
have gone,
All but one, that lies under a stone;
Fly thee home, Lady-Bird, ere it
be gone.

THE LOVING BROTHERS

I love you well, my little brother,
And you are fond of me;
Let us be kind to one another,
As brothers ought to be.
You shall learn to play with me,
And learn to use my toys;
And then I think that we shall be
Two happy little boys.

ONE, TWO.

One, two,
Buckle my shoe;
Three, four,
Knock at the door;
Five, six,
Pick up sticks;
Seven, eight,
Lay them straight;
Nine, ten,
A good fat hen;
Eleven, twelve,
Who will delve;
Thirteen, fourteen,
Maids a-courting;

15.16.
17.18.
19.20.

Fifteen, sixteen,
Maids in the kitchen;

Seventeen, eighteen,
Maids a-waiting;

Nineteen, twenty,
My plate 's empty.

A
was an
apple pie
B
bit
it,
C
cut
it,
D
dealt
it;
E
eat
it,
F
fought
for it,
G
got
it;
H
had
it,
J
joined
it:
K
kept
it,
L
longed
for it,
M
mourned
for it,